for Ne ...

Happy memories
of February 10, 2015

Leo Aylen

SILVER BOOK BOX

RHYMOCEROS

Leo Aylen

MACMILLAN

Silver Book Box
Series Editor: Julia Eccleshare

Contents

Acknowledgements

'The Rhymoceros' was performed by Leo Aylen on BBC TV (*Playschool*) in 1984. The programme has been repeated a number of times. 'Ant fantasy' was performed by Leo Aylen on BBC TV (*Walrus*) in 1987. The following poems are published in anthologies: 'The undistinguished visitor' in *Spaceways*, OUP, 1986; 'The tidy burglar' in *Standpoints*, Harrap, 1983; 'Stage-struck' in *A Fifth Poetry Book*, OUP, 1985; 'The tramp who told stories' (in an earlier version called 'Kitchen adventure') in *Another Second Poetry Book*, OUP, 1988; 'Somewhere in the sky' in *Another Third Poetry Book*, OUP, 1988.

Three poems are reprinted from collections by Leo Aylen, by permission of Sidgwick & Jackson: 'Seaside-and-merrygoround summer holiday' from *Sunflower*, 1976; 'Flop' from *Jumping-shoes*, 1983; 'Dog poem' from *Return to Zululand*, 1980.

'Micky Hackett's rocket' and 'Poetry is...' are published in *Poetry Express No. 15*, October 1987.

Leo Aylen has performed the *The Rhymoceros Show* in many children's theatres, libraries, and schools. The show is frequently followed by a workshop in which children write poems inspired by the show. The poems printed on pages 11, 16, 17, and 27, have been chosen out of hundreds, to give an idea of what children can do themselves.

If you want to read more poetry by Leo Aylen, his other poetry books are: *I, Odysseus*; *Sunflower*; *Return to Zululand*; *Red Alert: this is a god warning*; *Jumping-Shoes*. They are published by Sidgwick & Jackson Ltd.

PART I

POETRY IS...

Poetry is .... Imagination

Suppose your doormat is a jungle full of dragonmice and chimpanzeebras . . .

THE RHYMOCEROS

Does he gallop sideways, snorting,
                            through the nostrils in his tail?
Is his tummy custard-coloured?
                            Does he leave a slimy trail?
Does he rattle when he gargles?
                            Does he have eleven toes?
Does he talk like a Chicago gangster
                            t'rough his ndose?
Does he howl? Or sort of mumble?
                            Are his feet like p'liceman's boots?
Is his left hind leg bright purple?
                            Are his claws as huge as roots?
Is his favourite colour yellow?
                            Is his favourite colour blue?
Does he chirp, squawk, squeak, roar, bellow,
                            bark, bleat, miauow, or moo?
Does he fly, hop, crawl, or burrow?
                            Does he have fur, scales, or wings?
Is he spotted, striped, or dotted?
                            Does he bite? Perhaps he stings.

Does he live on Christmas pudding
                    and chocolate-coated kippers?
Does he prefer fresh ostrich eggs
                    and toasted bedroom slippers?
Does he charge full tilt at houses,
                    and crash through locked front doors?
Or is he wee and timorous,
                    hiding in chests-of-drawers?
Can he change himself to a wheelchair?
                    A clock? A tin of peaches?
Does he crawl up you like spiders?
                    Or bite your leg like leeches?
Or is he like a spaniel –
                    tail-wag, tongue-lick, and lollopy,
Asking for his dinner
                    which he gobbles sloppy-gollopy?

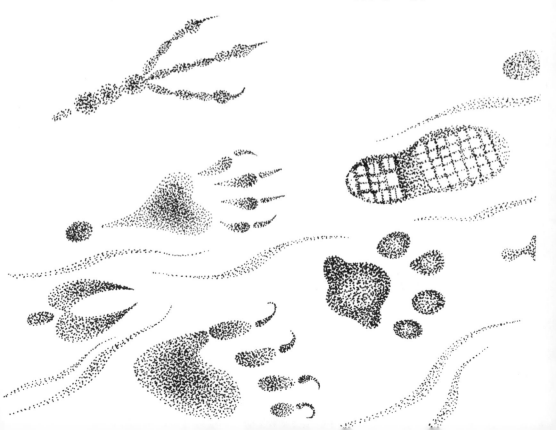

I know he raggles every night.
                I think he mowgles too.
He's hooshy, and scroorooshy,
                and sometimes floogoroo.
He'll barl you, and kemarl you,
                and klownder through the grame.
And never, ever, ever,
                will he answer to his name.

He'll cronk, he'll shonk, he'll tronk you,
                he'll gloogle till you're frothed.
He'll fattle, and spewrattle,
                he'll blettifaze your loft.
He'll ossify your akkelard,
                and make you take the blame.
And never, ever, ever,
                will he answer to his name.

For gruntage and ploombuntage
                there's nothing like his nibs.
He'll vogglefade and ruggleslide,
                and voooooomble bronderbibs.
His gundersnag is proflikop,
                his carmoral's like flame.
And never, ever, ever,
                will he answer to his name.

You can call him,
Bawl him,
Caterwaul him,
Trawl him,
Maul him,
Overhaul him,
You'll just appal him, and he'll never answer to his name.

But if you can doggle,
Cloggle,
Or balmoggle,
If you dare spreckle
Your feckles
With greckle,
If, with a spoon-
ful of thistle
And wild boar bristle
You whistle
His tune
At the full moon
And listen ...
It's possible ...
You might see climb ...
Like a colossal
Fossil,
With grime,
Slime, an' moss across
His lime phosphorus
Gossamer chrysalis –

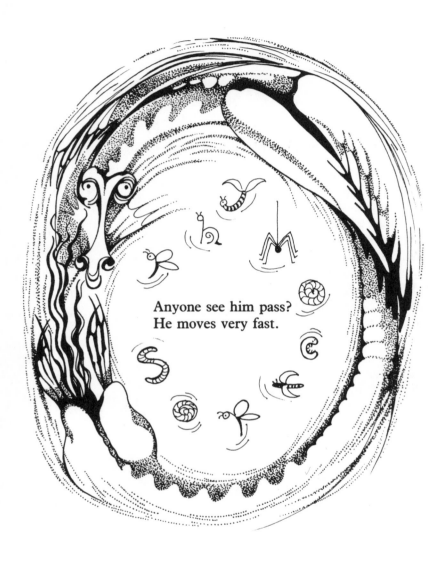

Anyone see him pass?
He moves very fast.

Well, if you see him again,
Ask him to be your friend.
The end.

TWO CHILDREN'S MONSTERS

These two monster poems were written by children in a Manchester primary school: Ronald Wells and Jayne Rooney.

His name is Rollo, and he likes the night,
Flies in circles, making patterns in the sky.
He has a head like an egg.
Round his eye is an orange, red and yellow pattern.
On his body you can see markings as you can on his horn.
Round and round he goes,
Taking apples off the trees,
Swallowing them whole,
Watch out for your dog when he's around.
He'll steal him away and drop him in the water.
If you want him to go away, find a mouse if you can.
He won't come near in case it bites his toe.
At night Rollo sleeps in a cave in the hills.

Does it mumble in the jungle?
Does it give a nasty bite?
Are his teeth red, green and blue?
When he sneezes does he say 'Bless you!'
Does he have a nasty cough?
Or does he dribble on and off?
Has he got shiny claws?
Or are they dirty like the dinosaurs?
Does he walk on his twenty toes?
Are they hairy? Nobody knows.
Does he rattle in a battle?
Or does he winkle with a twinkle?
Does he shout hurray all day?
Or does he hide away and pray?

Poetry is ....Alliteration

Letting **Letters** *lick your lollipops while they leapfrog over you from London to Land's End, without losing your luggage or your laundry . . .*

UNCLE GEORGE AND THE gg's

Uncle George woke up one morning
        with a very strange disease.
He found he could only do things
        that began with letter 'G's'.
He could goggle and gurgle and gargle,
        gawp and grin and grunt.
He could gallop and gollop and gossip,
        and glue things back to front.
He could gamble, and gambol up gangways,
        or dance an old-fashioned gavotte.
But he couldn't boil his kettle
        or put the tea in the pot.
His cornflakes tasted gritty;
        gravy gushed over his toast.
He ate golden syrup and gingernuts,
        and couldn't read his post.
He wrapped himself in a groundsheet –
        he couldn't wear his suit –
He put on his gloves and galoshes.
        His wife said, 'You look cute.'

He gave his guinea-pigs groundsel
        and cleaned his garden gnomes.
But his hair was a mess because
        he couldn't use brushes or combs.
He couldn't drive to the office,
        or catch a train or a bus.
So he grovelled there with a gorilla
        from the London Zoo called Gus.
He couldn't sit down in his office.
        He glided into the gym,
Giving orders that gadgets and grievances
        should be brought there to him.
His secretary said, 'Mr Grant
        dictates with such perfect grammar.
I know he gabbles and gibbers,
        but at least he doesn't stammer.'
When the others went out to lunch
        George gobbled grilled gammon and
        Guinness.
He had to refuse when prim Mrs Dews
        said, 'Innyone for tinnis,'
'Cos he couldn't play tennis or cricket or squash,
        and certainly not football.
All he could do was bowl googlies
        against the garden wall.
Poor George became grizzled and grumpy;
        he started gnawing his gnails;
Especially now as the weather
        seemed to be nothing but gales.
They'd find him grieving in graveyards
        playing Gluck on his glockenspiel.
Even the gargoyles guffawed:
        'The guy's got no feel.'

But on a grand, golden evening,
               while goats were grazing the grass,
A girl-guide, giggling gushingly,
               gave George a glittering glass
Of gooseberry and grape juice.
               'Drink it' she said, and grinned.
Glug, glug! Ooh! George felt giddy.
               He groaned. A gigantic wind
Blew him into a grimy grotto,
               greasy, grey-green, grotesque,
Where a grisly ghost sat grimacing
               at a government office desk.
'George,' said the ghost, 'here's a riddle,
               which you are obliged to guess.
If you guess right, why, yes, tonight,
               you'll be cured of your G-sickness.
So tell me the meaning of this song
When I sound the gong:

Dong:

'Auntie's butter cookies do easily fry.
Happy Indian junior kings
Love munching naughtily orange pie.
Quickly Robin sings
To Uncle Victor whose eXercise
Yanks zither-strings.'

14

Then George said 'Gosh!' and 'Golly!' and 'Gee!'
'It's tosh,
But its jolly,
And I'm free!
'Cos not one word
Of your riddle rhyme
Begins with the letter "G".'

Uncle George taught all of us
                              the riddle of the grey-green ghost,
In case we should come down to breakfast,
        and find grey globules of glutinous, gungy gruel,
            instead of cornflakes, marmalade, and toast.
So please keep Uncle George happy by saying after me
The riddle which set him free:

'Auntie's Butter Cookies Do Easily Fry.
Happy Indian Junior Kings
Love Munching Naughtily Orange Pie.
Quickly Robin Sings
To Uncle Victor Whose eXercise
Yanks Zither-strings.'

Have you guessed what the riddle means?

CHILDREN'S WORK
WITH LETTERS

A girl called Pippa Watson, at a school in Clwyd, wrote this Letter Disease story, and the crocodile alphabet was done by a girl in an infants' school near Chester.

Bertie bought a beautiful bunch of big bananas, but when he reached Betty's bungalow she had banished him from entering. He went to Brian's big house and was banned from going in. But he went to his best bench in the buttercup field. He opened the bag with the beautiful bunch of big bananas in, but all the bananas were bad, bruised, battered, broken and bumped. Bertie was baffled. Bertie had a brilliant brainwave: he bombed it breathlessly to Barclays Bank where he asked Boris Barley if he could borrow 1 billion pounds in a big black bin bag. Boris Barley said Bertie could borrow 1 billion pounds, but in a big blue bin bag, not a big black bin bag. Bertie was brainless with joy. Bertie bombed it out of Barclays Bank building and into the banana shop, where he bought billions of bunches of bananas. He made sure they weren't bruised, battered, broken and bumped. Bertie went to Betty's bungalow, where he bashfully gave Betty 60 bunches of the biggest bananas he had. Bertie went to Brian's house and brainlessly gave him 3 bunches that just happened to be bruised, battered, broken and bumped. While Betty and Brian were going barmy with each other, bopping, boxing and bashing each other, Bertie biked it to Belgium.

16

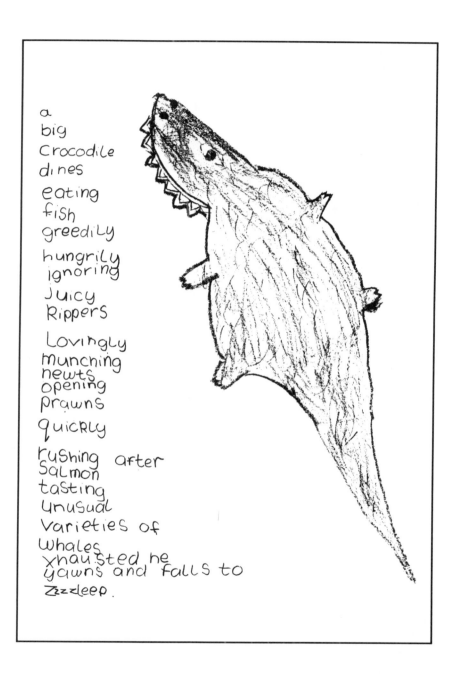

a
big
Crocodile
dines
eating
fish
greedily
hungrily
ignoring
Juicy
Rippers

Lovingly
munching
newts
opening
prawns

quickly

rushing after
salmon
tasting
unusual
varieties of
whales
xhausted he
yawns and falls to
zzzleep.

Poetry is ... Sounds

The **sound** *of syllables being tickled till they giggle and jump about, kicking their legs in the air . . .*

MICKY HACKETT'S ROCKET

Micky Hackett
Built a rocket
From a bracket
And a sprocket.
'Look, Dicky! Book your ticket.'
Dicky tried to nick it.
'I'll knock it,
Kick it,
Crack it.'
They were making such a racket,
Dad took it,
Tried to pack it
In the pocket
Of his jacket.

But Mick – 'e's quick an' wicked –
Said, 'Dick, let's see you dock it.
Sneak it out and hook it
To the cooker.
Stick it
Crooked
In the socket
And tack it.'
Wow! What a shock! It
Knocked Dad back. It
Crackled,
Smoked, and blackened
A mackerel,
Some cheese crackers,
Dad's mac, a tennis racquet,
And a packet of Mum's stockings.
Mum raised a raucous ruckus,
Smacked 'em, made 'em chuck it
All mucky in the bucket.
Dad whacked 'em,
Thwacked 'em,
Kicked 'em
Up to their room and locked it.

OUR ART TEACHER

Latterly
Old Mr Satterly
Looks utterly
Shattered.
His teeth chatter.
He stutters,
Mutters,
'Can't stand clutter,'
Then drops fish-guts
For cats in gutters,
Lets
Litters
Of kittens
Wet
On his letters.
He bets,
Sells lottery
Tickets in pottery
Classes,
Wears grotty
Glasses,
Spats,
And mittens.

He spits.
He's tottery,
Doddery,
Blows
His nose
On his blotter,
Empties his potty
In the street.
He's dotty,
Batty,
Scatty.
He can't eat
Batter,
Fat,
Butter,
Pig's trotters
Or potted meat.
He's a rat.
He's always tight.
But in spite
Of that,
I think he's sweet.

ANT FANTASY

In Santa Claus' pantry
An ant, of noted gallantry,
Who'd joined up in the infantry,
Was drinking Asti Spumante –
More allegro than andante –
With the Infanta of Shantung,
When Santa
Grabbed the decanter,
Wantonly tripped on his reindeer's antler,
And panted, 'Let's have some fun.'
But out of the Atlantic,
With eyes as huge as lanterns,
A hideous, gigantic,
Antipodean, tarantula
Triumphantly hissed 'Tantara!
You all shall be my banquet:
You Ant, you drunk old Santa,
And you, fragrant Infanta,
Sweet as a currant bun.'
'You termagant antagonist,'
The ant replied, shaking his fist,
'The Infanta is my niece.'

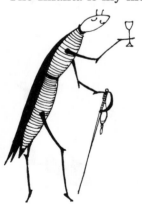

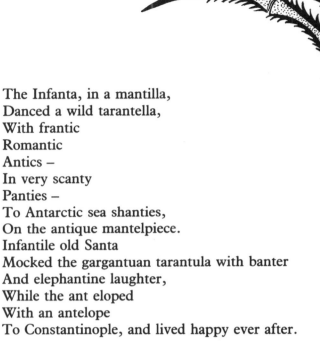

The Infanta, in a mantilla,
Danced a wild tarantella,
With frantic
Romantic
Antics –
In very scanty
Panties –
To Antarctic sea shanties,
On the antique mantelpiece.
Infantile old Santa
Mocked the gargantuan tarantula with banter
And elephantine laughter,
While the ant eloped
With an antelope
To Constantinople, and lived happy ever after.

This poem was specially written for the BBC Schools TV series Walrus.
It had to contain as many words as possible with the syllable 'ant' in them.

Poetry is ...Images

Like having a television set inside your head, with the sound off.
Riddle poems are one way of playing with images.

RIDDLE 1

The blackened spearhead of crushed plants
Stabs at the snowy surface of the flattened forest,
Leaving footmarks for two lensed jellies to decipher.
The black point slides back inside the hollow tree.
But the tree, pirouetting in the grinder,
Gives birth to another spear
Ready to scar the unmarked whiteness.

RIDDLE 2

He pressed on the end of the rocket casing.
A soft pink worm
Peeped its head to the light,
Then stretched asleep on top of the forest
Attached to his crowbar.
His face appeared in the window.
Beneath it he opened
The gleaming sluice of the dam, and the river gushed out.
Gently he led both worm and forest
Down to the water to drink and bathe.
Then, lifting his crowbar,
He shoved it into his mouth,
And crushed the body of the worm to bubbles.

RIDDLE 3

On to the flame she placed
A gong, a clashing cymbal,
A huge steel ping-pong bat,
And spread on it a pair of striped pink trousers.
The ping-pong ball
Was a bald-headed man.
She ordered his execution.
Crash, and his jaw was broken.
Transparent lymph gushed out. No blood.
The forest was crackling,
The volcano bubbling;
She laid the man beside his trousers,
And he became the sun shining through white clouds.

Would you have guessed the answer to these riddles without the pictures?

CHILDREN'S RIDDLES

These two riddles were composed by teenage girls.
This first one was by Esme Parry and Joanna Grey Lloyd,
working together:

From the steaming jacuzzi
The featureless face rolls out
And lands on the throne.
With a deafening murderous blow
The sledgehammer smashes the crown,
And the dried paint cracks,
Revealing the eclipsed sun in its colourless vault.

(Cracking a hard-boiled egg)

This one was by Ann Irvin and a partner.

Two massive waterfalls
Crashing and swirling into a deep cavern.
Then a great anchor secured itself into the depths.
A bright green laser pierces the film of the ocean.
Glistening crystals of air emerge;
A flash of white appears —
And a U.F.O. plunges into the unknown,
Submerging into a strange liquid.
Suddenly it reappears, reaching to the sky,
Bright, clean and shining —
But comes to land on the banks of the great unknown.

(Washing up a plate)

Poetry Is ... Fantasy

Pushing **images** *around inside you, like switching on the television inside your head, turning up the sound, and watching all the channels at the same time.*

DOTTIDREEM 1

Last night I drove a dodgem car
Across an Indian plain.
A man with tadpoles in a jam-jar
Said, 'Why not go by train?'

A monkey, riding a camel, tried
To steal my sandwich box.
But all that we could find inside
Was tiny alarm clocks.

'Haven't you tasted alarm clocks?' said
A woman on a elephant.
'You can eat them with cheese, or chocolate spread.'
But I cried 'Shan't, I shan't.'

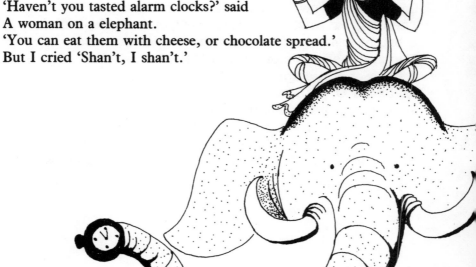

The man with the tadpoles shouted out,
'You naughty, spoilt, young thing!
Eat your alarm-clocks, or I'll clout
You one with my bee-sting.'

I drove my dodgem very fast.
He chased me on his bee.
Try as he would, he couldn't get past.
So he started shooting at me.

The bullets were whizzing round my nose.
But the camel-riding ape
Shouted, 'Quickly! Touch your toes.
That's how you can escape.'

I touched my toes and swam away
Like a fish in lemonade.
Then Mum looked in, and I heard her say,
'My! What a mess you've made.'

DOTTIDREEM 2

Last night I dreamt a chimpanzee
Knocked on our kitchen door,
Asked, 'May I borrow a packet of tea?'
Then emptied it on the floor.

I yelled, 'Come here, you stupid ape,'
And chased him down the street.
But when I thought he couldn't escape,
I found I had three feet,

And one of my feet was kicking the others
As hard as it possibly could.
I said, 'Be nice to your nice brothers.'
It said, 'Brothers! They're no good.'

The chimp came back with a fireman's hose,
And soaked us all to the skin.
It said, 'If you can breathe through your nose,
You can be a fire engine.'

Suddenly, up the road they came –
Six fire engines in red.
One shouted, 'I'm playing a pantomime dame,'
Saluted, and stood on its head.

The other five became quite cross,
And started unrolling their ladders.
'No actor will ever be our boss,'
They hissed like angry adders.

But the chimpanzee simply waved his hand:
The fire engines disappeared.
Chimp whispered, 'I'm off to Bongoland,'
And vanished in his own beard,

As I woke up, while in our street
Three fire engines went past.
'Look Mum! I've only got two feet.'
'Come on,' she said. 'Breakfast!'

DOTTIDREEM 3

I dreamt an owl sat on my bed
And tried to sing a song.
He was out of breath. His face was red.
He said, 'I won't be long.

'But I have to learn the proper tune,
And I mustn't forget the words.
I can't have 'em saying this afternoon
"What d'you expect with birds?"'

'Mr Owl,' I said, 'I'll teach you to sing.
Come to the piano, quick.'
But the piano keys unwound like string.
Owl said, 'That's a good trick.

'Wind up the notes again,' said Owl,
Into little balls of wool.
Then, when I stand up straight and howl,
You give each one a pull,

'And it'll unwind and turn my howl
Into a note in tune.'
'You stupid bird,' I said, 'You growl.
You'll never learn to croon.'

'Let me tell you,' the owl replied,
'I've starred in pantomime.'
'Mr Owl, your voice is a joke,' I cried,
'And you never, ever, keep time.'

Then Owl flew at me in a terrible rage.
I grabbed a conductor's baton.
We had a swordfight all over the stage.
I kept my woolly hat on.

I fenced the owl up against a wall.
He changed to a saxophone
Which sang in the way that babies bawl,
Or people in agony groan –

Louder and louder, a terrible noise,
Like a siren more or less.
Then I heard Mum saying, 'Boys will be boys.
But – oh my! – what a mess!'

Poetry is ... Words

Words dipping their fingers in the honey, and giving you some to lick . . .

SEASIDE-AND-MERRYGOROUND SUMMER HOLIDAY

On apricot saddles we'll ride this summer,
Lassooing the sunshine with streamers of peaches,
Hats full of haycocks, and walnut-patch britches,
With moonshine-melon-and-seagull-swoop trimmings.

Who's for a sandcastle picnic with splodge?
Splodge in the mud, and splodge in the honey.
I'll treat you – the joy-stalls sell joy for a penny.
Let's joy-lick our joy-sticks and fly off the edge.

Let's spinnaker-whistle through summer's spray,
Till we pull down the sunset stuck on to our kites.
Oh what monkey-tail-jumper and cat-pouncer nights.
What carousel-cantering-springboard days.

A WHITEWIZARD CHRISTMASNEWYEAR LITTLEPEOPLE SPELL

Like ant-eyed scurryings through moss and fern
By creatures man-scorched from their woods and streams
May every blessing from your past return
To bestow blessing on your future dreams.

Like Erlking exiles who've refused to learn
The master drumbeat in his misty themes
May every blessing from your past return
To bestow blessing on your future dreams.

Like ghosts of prayer just possible to discern
Through Giant Gobblegreedy's cake and creams
May every blessing from your past return
To bestow blessing on your future dreams.

POETRY IS...

...what makes you,
Long since buried,
Sneak out of your coffin, out of the graveyard,
To be caught on street corners
Playing exuberantly on a xylophone
You've built from the bones of your skeleton.

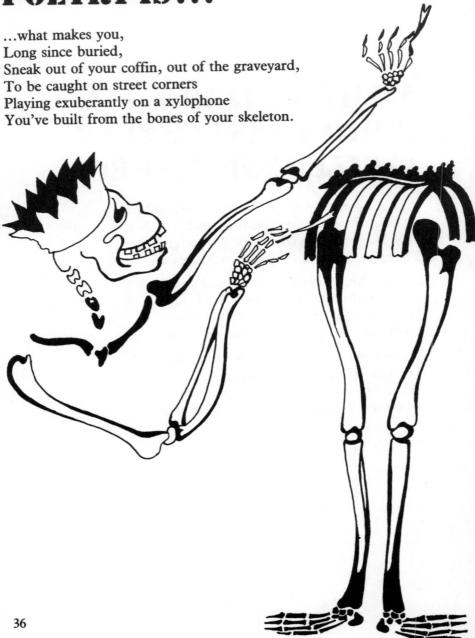

36

PART II

MORE POEMS

SOMEWHERE IN THE SKY

Somewhere
In the sky,
There's a door painted blue,
With a big brass knocker seven feet high.
If you can find it,
Knock, and go through –
That is, if you dare.
You'll see behind it
The secrets of the universe piled on a chair
Like a tangle of wool.
A voice will say,
'You have seven centuries in which to unwind it.
But whatever
You do,
You must never,
Ever,
Lose your temper and pull.'

THE TRAMP WHO TOLD STORIES

Out of matchsticks –
The tramp created a temple.

Out of cabbage-leaves –
An expedition lost in the jungle.
A beetle became a jackal.
Hyena laughter covered the kitchen table like spilt soup.

The boy obliged him by calling him 'Grandad',
And shrinking in size
To a couple of millimetres tall.

Some hours –
And a great many helicopter-whirrings by the boy's mother – later,
They were found by the search party,
Crossing a butter-dish glacier,
Luckily, both uninjured.

THE UNDISTINGUISHED VISITOR

'But I'm nothing unusual,' he said.
'My life is utterly undistinguished.
I've invented nothing, composed no symphonies,
Designed no temples, bridges, or palaces.
Until today I've hardly travelled –
Only to planets less than twenty light-years distant,'
Said the anthropoid with scarlet fur and telescopic eyes,
Who could hear a bat squeak from a mile away,
Outcalculate our largest computer,
And run forty miles in an hour on his seven-toed feet.
'To be frank,' he continued, 'they chose me
As being especially stupid,
And therefore suitable for leaving behind from the real expedition,
To investigate this planet of yours,
Which we call Garbage-Bucket.'

FLOP

In a bucket of black water
Was reflected a star.
'Stars are enormous, lad,
And ever so far.'

While the boy was watching,
Their donkey called Flop
Stuck his head in the bucket of water,
And drank every drop.

'Dad, what marvellous creatures
Little donkeys are.
Flop's belly is extra-terrestrial.
It can swallow a star.'

THE TIDY BURGLAR

The burglar tiptoed across the lawn,
That was cut like a carpet, sprinkler-smooth,
Past ornamental waterfall,
And pale blue, utterly algae-free, pool,

Crossed the patio, brushed past vines
Dripping with bunches of ripe, black grapes,
Cracked a window, stepped inside,
Admired the decanters, the velvet drapes,

Examined the stereo, touched the pictures,
Feeling the texture of the roughened oil paint,
Opened a cabinet with Georgian silver
And Tudor miniatures in intricate frames,

But took nothing. He went upstairs
To the master-bedroom's jewellery cases:
A diamond collar, six rings, a rare
Black pearl, some rubies, a dozen bracelets.

His eyes strayed to the rumpled bed.
Untidiness always drove him frantic.
He made it neatly, stacked cushions at the head,
Then, hearing a noise, left empty-handed.

This is a true story.

JUST ANOTHER TRIFLING MURDER

The Chief Inspector,
Wearing a Mickey-Mouse mask,
Arrived on a tricycle,
Waving his laser-gun.
The villain, disguised as Spiderman,
Had crashed through the greenhouse roof
Onto a tray of tomatoes laid out for the flower-show.
His crime – attempted manslaughter
Of one Susie Watkins
By drowning in a bowl of trifle –
Was pushed aside by huge woman-hands
Applying Dettol and Elastoplast.

FANCY-DRESS PARTY

'I have gambolled with elephants in bright yellow wellies,
Capered on a carpet spread thickly with jellies,
Been mauled by giraffes eating toffee sausage-rolls,
Then pelted with pies by three Toads, Rats and Moles.
My pockets are full of what feels like porridge.
On an Eskimo's orders I'm now off to forage
For chocolate-cake rations to feed a brigade
Of guardsmen, crusaders, and – what's this? – Band-Aid! –
Quick! Somebody's cut! Her sister is crying.
Give me some Dettol. Tracy, stop trying
To scrub Kevin's shirt with lemon meringue.
Isn't it time that everyone sang
Some nice old song like "There's no place like home"
And then went home quickly – Yes, here's your comb,
Leslie – 'cos I'm finished – just like this pome.'

CHRISTMAS DINNER

The green lop-sided uncles with onions in their cheeks
Are drinking pale green brandy made from nail-varnish and leeks.
Pale aunts like Elastoplast keep patching up the cuts
And propping them up from falling drunk into water butts.
What a *very* happy party with the fam'ly all together,
Everybody talking about last Christmas's weather
And their various diseases in anatomical detail,
And how when buying clothes none of them pay retail.
The cakes and puddings gather round that we're supposed to scoff.
One by one they swallow us, with a little burp and cough,
The gold-wrapped chocolates crawl up us with insect scratchings,
While Uncle Wilf, falling asleep, murmurs,

        'Come and see my etchings,'
Till – no more family – the uncles all disposed of,
Out-pudding'd, ev'ryone...even me...has dozed...off... .

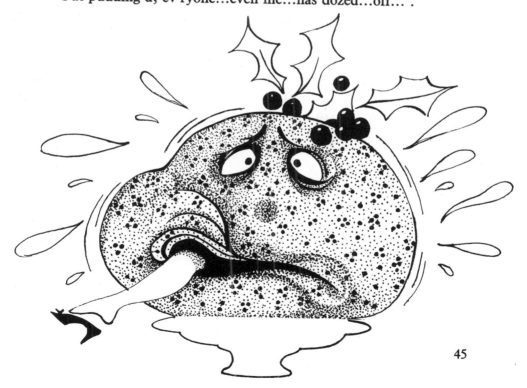

STAGE-STRUCK

'Well then, young Darryl,' said Uncle Tom,
'What do you want to be when you grow up?'
'An actor.' 'An ahktoor. That's right champion.'
Uncle Tom struck himself in the gut.

'Did I ever tell you, young Darryl,' he mouthed,
'How I once played York in *Richard the Second*
For the Batley Town Council Players. Pow!
I went through that audience like a Black-an'-Decker.

'But you, young Darryl, you'll want to play Richard,
Richard himself, then Hamlet, then Lear –
The climax of every actor's ambition.
I'm sure you'll move your audience to tears.

'I'm right glad, Darryl. So few young chaps
Are moved by the ring of Shakespeare's lines.
'To be or not to be ...,' eh lad, that's
The stuff to drive you out of your mind.'

'Well uncle, I wasn't thinking of Shakespeare,
More like of being a teevee star,
And making commercials in Las Vegas
For Flora and Mannikin Cigars.'

LOOKING AT A PHOTO OF GRANDFATHER AS A BOY, WHILE HE RAMBLES ON, HALF OUT OF HIS MIND

Oh, once he ran,
Snatched blessing from the air
Like blossom from his bounding trees.
Now, no longer boy with apple hair,
He peers, a bent old man,
And scratches, on his knees,
For blessing under stones.
At last he hears his own voice drone:
'Neither the blessing nor yourself
Can be found anywhere.'

THUNDERSTORM

'Sky, you're hanging in the air
Like a wet fish.
I wish
That you had bare
Feet to run over the sand,
And play races with me,' said the boy.
From outer space, a hand
Clouted the boy on the head
With a huge black cloud,
And shouted out:
'You were starting to annoy
Me, you foolish child.
Now, you've got me riled.'
The boy turned pale
As the sky started pelting him
With small white pebbles like hail.

MAYFLY OUT OF CADDIS-WORM

'Watch', he said, 'that mayfly darting,
Flashing, flickering, in the dazzle-froth
Of river-reflection, as you hold in your hand
This grit and pebble-fragment caddis-worm-cover.
This creature wraps itself in rock-splinter
To wait for its hour of wingborn life.
For its streambottom crawl it wears the earth.
For its moment of loving it bears the sky.'

The mayfly lives only for a few hours in its winged state. It has no means of eating. It exists only to mate, lay eggs, and die. The larva is known as a caddis-worm, and wraps itself up in a case of grit and tiny pebbles, which serves as both protection and camouflage as it lies at the bottom of the pond or stream.

DOG POEM

Driving my little dog-cart
Along the Dogger Bank,
I met the Doge of Venice,
(A man of dogal rank).
While he expounded dogma
In vile-rhymed doggerel,
We walked through dog-toothed arches
To a dog-cheap hotel.
There, as the evening dog-star
Rose o'er the dogwood tree,
I grumbled, 'Doge of Venice,
You argue doggedly.
But I'm here to lie doggo;
Besides, I'm quite dog-tired.'
He shouted in dog-latin:
'Doggone it, boy! You're fired.'

The poet Charles Causley wrote a poem which begins:

> *As I went down the catwalk*
> *Where all the catkins blow.*

In every line of the poem there is a word which includes the syllable 'cat'.
Charles Causley has a cat, so he wrote a cat poem. I have a dog, so I wrote
a dog poem in reply.

PART III

A STORY POEM

This story-poem is a retelling of an old Norse legend. The Norse gods were unlike other gods. They were not immortal: they knew that they would grow old and die, unless they kept themselves young by eating magic apples every day. This story of how the apples were stolen by the eagle giant of the frozen north, is a summer and winter story: summer's fruit which makes us feel young is stolen by icy winter. But the apples are rescued, and summer returns.

THE APPLES OF YOUTH

In ancient times there were ancient gods,
Who lived in a city in the sky.
There was Thor, the god of thunderclouds,
Tyr, the war-god, Frey,
And All-father Odin, who was wise and good,
But only had one eye.

Each morning they met to rule the world
In a palace with golden thrones.
Then they hunted and wrestled, and swam in the cold
Sea water, and raced on sharp stones,
And, whatever they did, they never grew old –
No aches, no creaking bones.

For during every afternoon
A golden-haired goddess, called Idun,
Arrived with her basket of magic apples,
And sang to a snappy little tune:

'Take a bite,
Take a bite,
Take a bite,
Take a nibble of my apples,
And your happiness will bubble
Double bright.
You'll grapple with your troubles,
Never dribble, never hobble,
Never stop, trip, flop, or wobble,
As you bob along the river of delight.

One sip
Of my juice
Makes you loose and supple;
You'll be lighter than a petal,
But your muscles – ooh – they'll ripple
Like snakes of glittering metal.
In your tussles you will topple
Every hustler that you wrestle.
In your battles you will cripple
Your attackers till they rattle.
You'll be fit enough to flatten
Tricky baddies into batter,
And with zip enough to dance all night.
So take a bite and shout:
"An apple a day keeps the doctor away,"
And that'll knock old age out.'

Every god who lived in the city
Munched his apple, and punched with power,
And every goddess looked as pretty
As an April flower.
Young, strong, beautiful, and wise,
They smiled at each other with happy eyes.

But there was a god called Loki,
Who was nasty and spiteful.
He was clever and joky,
But very deceitful.
His tricks
Made decent people sick.
In fact he was hateful.
His little eyes were mean; his nose was poky.

Loki went hunting. Whooosh! An eagle
Pounced like a flash of lightning.
Loki was caught. He tried to struggle.
The eagle's huge claws tightened.

In a deep bass voice the eagle snarled:
'I am the Giant of the Storm.
D'you want to be ripped in pieces and hurled
Like breadcrumbs over the corn?'

Loki was vicious; cowardly too.
'No, no,' said Loki. 'No, please.'
'Right,' said the giant, 'I want Idun.
Bring her and her apples to me.'

So Loki went back to the city of the gods,
And called on lovely Idun.
He sang in a voice that was creaky and odd,
To a slinky, horrible, tune:

'D'you know what I've found,
Idun, Idun?
Out on the high ground,
Idun, Idun?
Not far from the city?
It is such a pity
You don't know what I know, Idun.

'I've found an apple tree,
Sweet Idun,
With better fruit, you see,
Idun, than yours.
If you don't come with me,
Sweet Idun,
I think that it will be ...
Loki, who restores
Youth to the gods each afternoon,
While you sit weeping on a heap of mouldy apple cores.'

Idun was trusting, innocent, good.
She didn't know Loki was lying.
She followed him up through a mountainous wood
To a crag where the giant was flying.

The giant swooped – screech – he carried her off
To his castle of icy waste.
He growled with a rasping and hacking cough:
'Now give me an apple to taste.'

'My apples of youth will be kept for the gods,
Who are holy and brave and wise.
You, evil monster, the only food
I'd give you's a load of mud pies.'

The giant roared and screamed with rage:
'Come here and teach her a lesson.'
Ogres and trolls yellow with age,
Hideous giantesses,
Locked Idun in a tower,
Where they shouted for more than an hour:

'Yahbtheah!
You'll go out of your wits.
We will rip you to bits.
And bite you and munch you,
And chew you and crunch you,
With our jagged, dirty green, fangs.
Hand over the fruit,
Or we'll put in the boot,
And blast you with horrible bangs:
Yahbtheah!'

At the top of the tower, icy and cold,
They left Idun to freeze on her own.
Without her apples, the gods grew old.
They had pains in their backs, and aching bones.

There was no more wrestling, no more running,
No more swimming in the sparkly sea.
Jokes didn't seem to be half as funny,
And they found it harder to hear and see.

But they noticed Loki,
Sneaking away,
Trying to hide.
'Why are you looking so shifty today?'
They dragged him inside,
And started poking
Him in the ribs till he whimpered and cried:

'I done it. I'm the one to blame.
Please don't poke me any more.
The Giant of Storm
Has captured her. I'm so ashamed.
I'm so ashamed.'

'Stop snivelling, you nasty thing.
Pull yourself together.
D'you want a clout across the ear?
Put on this pair of falcon wings.
Fly to Idun, and bring her here.
It looks like good flying weather.'

So Loki turned into a falcon,
And flew to the north very fast.
If he'd tried to get there by walking,
He'd have stuck in the frozen marsh.

Idun looked out from between the bars
Of her prison, and sang to the stars:

'I want to be home.
I want to be giving
My friends a reason for living.
I want to be making them happy and young.
I want them running and leaping,
Not snoozing and sleeping.
I want them strong.
Evil always does well.
The good need help.
Oh how I long to be home.'

Suddenly – whooosh! –
Out of the sky,
Loki the falcon: 'Sssh' –
And he slipped through the bars –
'Are you ready to fly?
I'm changing you into a swallow gripped in my claws,
And your basket of apples into a nut.
Now let's get out.'

The falcon flew off as fast as he could,
But an ogre looked out of his icicle wood
And smelt there was something strange.
He hurried to find the giant of the storm,
Who was fishing for eels, and keeping warm
By chattering with rage.

They rushed to the tower to look for Idun.
No Idun, no apples. An empty room.
The giant spat storm from his mouth.
He changed himself to a racing eagle –
Each of his claws as sharp as a needle –
And flew like lightning south.

In their city the gods were up on the walls,
When through the hurricane rainstorm squalls
They noticed a tiny dot.
'Look! Loki the falcon!' Heimdal cried –
Heimdal had special, telescope, eyes –
'With a swallow holding a nut.'

But close behind was a larger speck.
'The eagle,' cried Heimdal. 'They're neck and neck.
Come on, Loki! Loki! Race!
The eagle's gaining every yard.
Come on, Loki, you're not trying hard
Enough, you're a disgrace.'

The gods grabbed logs, and piled them higher
And higher on the walls to build a fire.
'Stand by with the tinder and flint.'
'The eagle's almost on Loki's tail.
Loki's breath is beginning to fail.
C'mon, Loki! Loki! Sprint!'

Loki flopped over the city walls,
Collapsed on the ground in a gasping sprawl.
The eagle was flying too fast.
They lit the fire as he reached the top
Of the walls. He couldn't swerve or stop.
He hit the flames full blast.

He was burnt in a second to ashes.
The swallow turned back to Idun.
The nut turned back to her basket of apples,
And she sang to a quiet tune:

'You who are wise and good and brave,
Be young and strong again.
While evil spirits rave
Against us, and evil men
Scar the fair earth
With black destruction,
Here let there flourish long-forgotten mirth,
And the spring's resurrection.'

So the gods took a nibble,
Then a bite
Of the apples,
And happiness doubled
Overnight.
They tipped the troubles
Of the world on the rubbish-
Heap, and skipped in the ripples of the ocean of delight.
They forgave
The giant, and saved his eyes
To be stars in the sky
Because he was brave.
And then they sang
To me, to you, to everyone:

'Let youth remember every day
The miracle of being young.
Youth has a million games to play,
A million songs that can be sung.
So every day let youth make hymns
Of thanks for having supple limbs.'

May we, who still have strength and youth,
Use all our youth and strength and speed
To help the brave to speak the truth,
To help the weak and those in need,
And still have more strength left to praise
The sun for giving summer days.

So:
Take a bite,
Take a bite,
Take a bite,
Take a nibble of my apples,
And your happiness will bubble
Double bright.
You'll grapple with your troubles,
Never dribble, never hobble,
Never stop, trip, flop, or wobble,
As you bob along the river of delight.
One sip
Of my juice
Makes you loose and supple;
You'll be lighter than a petal,
But your muscles – ooh – they'll ripple
Like snakes of glittering metal.
In your tussles you will topple
Every hustler that you wrestle.
In your battles you will cripple
Your attackers till they rattle.
You'll be fit enough to flatten
Tricky baddies into batter,
And with zip enough to dance all night.
So take a bite and shout:
"An apple a day keeps the doctor away,"
And that'll knock old age out.'

First published in *Silver Book Box* 1989

Published by
MACMILLAN EDUCATION LTD
Houndmills, Basingstoke, Hampshire RG21 2XS
and London
Companies and representatives
throughout the world

Designed by Julian Holland

Illustrated by Julia Heseltine

Typeset by Vine & Gorfin Ltd,
Exmouth, Devon, England

Printed in Hong Kong

British Library Cataloguing in Publication Data
Aylen, Leo
Rhymoceros.—(Silver book box).
I. Title   II. Series
821
ISBN 0–333–47047–8